MAY IT BRIGHTEN

YOUR DAY

HEY, PEANUTS!

Selected Cartoons From
MORE PEANUTS
Vol. 2

by Charles M. Schulz

A Fawcett Crest Book

Fawcett Publications, Inc., Greenwich, Conn.
Member of American Book Publishers Council, Inc.

MY DAD BOUGHT ME A NEW GYM SET...

IT'S GOT TWO SWINGS ON IT A PARALLEL BAR, A TEETER-TOTTER, A PAIR OF RINGS AND A TRAPEZE...

ON THE SIDES IT'S GOT A BELL, A WATER SPRAY, A BASKETBALL HOOP, A SIREN, A SLIDE AND A BIG UMBRELLA

I'M SCARED TO GO NEAR THE THING!

SCHROEDER, HOW DO YOU MANAGE TO PLAY ALL THOSE GREAT PIECES ON A TOY PIANO?

YOU GOTTA GET THE BREAKS!

SCHULZ

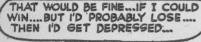

SCHULZ

AH? AH? AH?

AHCHOO!

SCHULZ

SCHULZ